Best wishes

Ken ~~~~~~~~

WHITECAPS
in the
MEADOW

GIL STEVENSON

DORRANCE & COMPANY
Philadelphia

The quotations from the Gospel of Nicodemus and the Protevangelion are reprinted by permission of Collins & World Publishing Company from *The Lost Books of the Bible and the Forgotten Books of Eden.* Copyright © 1926, 1927 by Alpha House, Inc.

The Scripture quotations in this publication are from the Revised Standard Version of the Bible, copyright 1946, 1952 and © 1971 by the Division of Christian Education of the National Council of the Churches of Christ in the U.S.A., and used by permission, except for John 15:9, quoted on p. 58 from the American Bible Society's *Good News for Modern Man.*

For you, with love.

PREFACE

Wyoming authors usually write reminiscences of pioneer days or old times on the ranch. I envy those who can write authentically of these matters; as an immigrant from New England, come late in life, I can only write of the Wyoming I know. The pioneers may or may not have picnicked at Veedauwoo, but I doubt if they were concerned with ecology on the journey from Hither to Yon, or if they stayed at a blue motel in Rock Springs (think what they missed!). Yet they, too, loved this wide land and the beauty of the sunset over the prairie, cherished their pets, and loved one another. And they, too, in the wild mountain springtime saw whitecaps in the meadow.

I hope the fact that this book contains three kinds of writing doesn't make it seem like a hodgepodge. All of them, at least, are by the same author. First, there is a collection of recent poems; then there is a Wyoming children's story; and, for readers of my poetry who might like to see some of my other writings, I have included a number of essays, the selection of which I have tried to limit to subjects of general and continuing interest. I have called this part of the book "Purrs and Scratches," after the column by that name which I have written both for our Unitarian Fellowship newsletter and the *Laramie Sentinel.*

"Port Everglades," however, was written while I still lived in New England about a decade ago, but I have been assured that since my visit my favorite seaport has changed very little.

Gil Stevenson

Howell, Wyoming
Spring, 1974

CONTENTS

I
WHITECAPS IN THE MEADOW

CONSTRUCTS

the solstice gone
the equinox not come
it is today
a nothing sort of date
blue cold and sunny
no milk no mail no paper
no special happening
in the cosmos
to set apart
this winter day
as that on which
a new year starts

the faces round
the breakfast table
were just the same
last year at supper
yet the tree came down
we put away
the Christmas lights
a year had ended
and begun again
since in the kitchen
a numbered artifact
on the wall
told us it did

yet as the hand
passed midnight then
did you not feel
the gentle bump
and change of air
as when you cross
the border from
a rectangle that's ours

to one that isn't
home is where
we named and marked it
on the map
and so's a year

SPRINGTIME RIVER

the horses fed
we pause to watch
the clouds catch fire
beyond our river
almost majestically
it roils and sweeps
through a fresh world
of islands lush
with springtime green
where wild ducks nest
and we admire
our private lake
and proud peninsula
where lately was
a shriveled pasture

just as my lilac bush
for the long warm days
of early summer
in our lawn at home
bestows its fragrance
and its beauty
on whoever's there
so now our river
swells and spills
and flows and floods
the land with life
it won't be long
before we have
an ordinary creek
and an ordinary bush

our land's between
the springtime river
and another stream

the flow of traffic
on the highway
does that stream too
I wonder have
a lush bestowing time
though it's never lovely
and it never flows
beyond its banks
perhaps it's doomed
to always be
an ordinary
stream of traffic

WHITECAPS

down from what arctic
desolation drives
this bitter wind
such gloomy ragged
clouds across
our springtime sky
chilling our spirits
and our bones
and our peaceful river
churning and swelling
to a stormy sea
where last week sprang
the sweet new grass

I see the whitecaps
in our meadow
and wonder what
tormented wild
forbidden land
has sent to us
so strange a gift
that in our mountains
I may walk
an ocean shore
which once I knew

RELUCTANT SPRING

The wind is raw. The sun is bright
And after supper it's still light.
The cats want in; there's snow tonight.

My love takes readings, and I'm told
It's warm. I must be getting old
Because my bones say that it's cold.

My Poki's purring as I pull
The comb through tufts of winter wool.
She will be shedding three bags full

Regardless; and in the windy park
The boys fly kites till after dark.
The girls wear shorts, though we remark,

"It's freezing!" But we do not go
By weather, but by seasons, so
We'll go play marbles in the snow.

On, for the long, warm, dreamy days
Of July sun and August haze,
When the weather and we are back in phase!

GARDENER

You'd never hear me yearn for snow
If what I plant were what would grow
And I could reap that which I sow.

I leaned my hoe against a tree
And heard a voice that said to me,
"Remember, when you plant your seed,
A flower's just a pretty weed;
And when you water, you can't pass
The weeds and nourish just the grass."

To bring back Eden, it would seem,
Still is every gardener's dream—
Though He ordained a different scheme.

GYMKHANA

the empty fairgrounds
are hot and dusty
in the blazing sun
but on this weekday
afternoon
our world is here

here good people
give themselves and time
to set the barrels
click the stopwatch
keep the score sheets
and flag the races
for laughing kids
on horses dashing
about their games

above the stables
behind the stands
the storms assemble
rumble and flash
and then march over
with cool wind
and pelting drops
and welcome shade
but soon move on
to bigger things

on the highway beyond
the semis roll
from half the world
with goods to feed
the other half
while still beyond
against the hills

the long trains move
coals to Newcastle
or sugar beets to Colorado
or Datsuns and Toyotas
to Detroit

beyond the rails
we glimpse our city
where important things
undoubtedly
are going on
since they no more
than trains or trucks
or summer storms
take notice that
all life is here
and this is where
the action is

YARD SONG

Rain, rain, come today!
Let me put this hose away.

You can do, in one small shower,
More than I can in an hour.

Though we dig the summer scene,
We like it with some springtime green.

Rain, rain, don't stay away!
The sun can shine another day.

BREAK

the sky is gentle
with a milder blue
and the big clouds lazy
with the summer's fullness
the fairground stands
are empty now
the barns deserted
the fat lambs
and champion steers
gone to their fates

the hay is in
and in the haze
of autumn wood smoke
the soft air
and kindly sun
the world stands still
and dreams awhile
why shouldn't we
go and do likewise

why cannot we
just rest and dream
and look across
the quiet river
and the ripened fields
to where the mountains
shape the sky
feel the earth's rhythms
and the way the seasons
take a break

WINTER

do we have
the cold bare earth
the naked trees
chill crystal nights
and short dark days
just so that we'll
enjoy the summer
or does the winter
have some virtues
of its own

I think our cats
are sweet and gentle
because that's how
we treat them
and the darkest days
we make our brightest
and most joyous
were our Lord's birthday
in some other season
we would have moved it

the soaring springtime
and its lilting green
the blossoming air
the swelling streams
the warmth and life
that surge anew
with the healing sun
are to us given
but when earth sleeps
we're on our own

COLD FIRE

into the vast
fierce glowing heart
of golden fire
no man could make
I gaze and wonder
what artifacts
and golden treasures
from such a furnace
we could mold
as would astonish
some archaeologist
ten centuries hence

with these volcanic
primal coals
we'll warm the world
and all its works
keep humming

the sky grows dark
the wind comes up
the snow drifts deep
and swirls and streaks
across the road
the sunset fades
but still I think
of what we'd do
with all that fire

EAST WIND

Strange wind that spills
Down the sunrise hills,
Say what tidings there be
Of the faraway sea
For my love and me.

It's not of the rain
That we're yearning to know,
Nor the depth and the drift
Of the fierce mountain snow,
But of shores of blue water
Where salt breezes blow
And the great fishes swim
And the great ships go.

Wind from the east,
Bring us at least
A breath of the sea
Where home used to be
For my love and me.

THE LINGUISTS

in the grand ballroom
of a plush hotel
in a major city
the doctors of philosophy
expound to one another
their theories of
communication
while a small Chinese girl
and my daughter
hand in hand
skip down the sidewalk
though they don't know
each other's tongues
I wonder what
their theory is

ITCHY

my daughters' current
pet's a worm
I wonder how
in their young hands
his fate compares
with how he'd do
in wormsville

TO EDNA MILLAY

I know my learning has strange gaps,
But how could I have let it lapse
To where I never even knew
That you loved me and I loved you?

Through your poems our spirits touch;
How I wish my own were such!
Now that you sleep, I wake and cry,
"Lady, where were you as years went by?"
Though the question is really, "Where was I?"

GIFT

Dead blossoms heavy on the air?
No, for these you do not care.
Exotic scents that cloy and cling?
Perfume, alas, is not your thing.

To woo a girl, some heart-shaped candy
Ordinarily is dandy,
But if I sabotage your diet
It's likelier there'd be a riot.

Sparkling jewels, pretty clothes?
You don't have much use for those—
Besides, I can't afford such loot.
How about an ugli fruit?

PLANS

Let's dream and scheme and make tomorrow
(Plans include no pain or sorrow)—
How much money can we borrow?

The winters never will be cold,
The sunsets all will be real gold,
And you and I will not grow old.

You don't believe such things can be?
You should have more faith in me!
(I put it in the specs, you see.)

COSMOLOGY

Poki my cat
what are your categories
where in your world-view
do I fit
am I to you
a kind of creature
or something unique
or somewhat of each

if there's a future
for your kind
it may be because
the way you order
the feline cosmos
differs from how
we order ours

HASTE

some poet said
that all things come
to him who waits
but I never met
the man who waited
nor ever learned
how he made out

we cannot wait
for springtime sun
to melt the snow
that halts our traffic
since we alone
of all earth's creatures
heed not the seasons
but must do our thing
regardless

all empires fall
their very power
is their undoing
yet still we slay
our enemies because
we cannot wait
and they can't either
so one of us
like winter's snow
must be removed

yet we're sustained
by living things
and we must wait
for them to grow
but even that
we seek to hasten

though our own lives
we would prolong because
for immortality
we cannot wait

HISTORIAN

He could tell you what went on
In Ahab's day in old Shumron
Or Nebuchadnezzar's Babylon.

He could tell you every ploy
Of Helen's Greece or Priam's Troy
That made the gods them both destroy.

But what of today's affairs of men
Could this distinguished scholar pen?
He said, "Things were no different then."

FOR ELSA

did the scheme of things
require a car
to kill the playmate
of a gentle cat
and the pet and playmate
of my daughter
I said then please
look elsewhere for
someone to argue
that the scheme is right
though the final kindness
of the girl who found her
and made her grave
and let us know
was also in
the scheme of things

she was a small
gray tiger cat
the kind of kitten
that one gives away
part Siamese
the people said
and from the way
she romped and played
and talked with us
I can believe it
our hearts still carry
the love she gave us
and the fun we had
but you can't hold
a memory
and feel it purr

RASCAL

well may you ask
what kind of cat
on stubby legs
with small soft feet
has run to greet me
so I explain
his round blue eyes
long silky fur
great bushy tail
and tufted ears
make him a lynxel
and that of course
is one half lynx
and one half squirrel

well may you ask
what use are lynxels
what value has
a funny fuzzy
little cat
so I explain
that lynxels know
the greatest secret
in the world
a secret that
we humans learn
sometimes too late
a lynxel cat
knows how to love

MORNING STAR

When all the other stars have fled
Before the dawn and gone to bed,
One still shines in the pale green light
Between the mountains and the night.

When dawn retreats before the day,
I do my thing; she goes her way.
And when we're deep in sleep, it seems,
My love and I have separate dreams.

Swim on, bright planet! By your light,
Between the daytime and the night,
When you shine as the morning star,
My love and I together are.

A PUSSY FOR THE LIGHT

It's Halloween; this spooky night
A cat face masks the front porch light.
I made the first when you were small,
But now that you are growing tall
You still insist that on this night
I make a pussy for the light.

I'm sure that there will always be
Someone to trim a Christmas tree
Though you grow up and move away—
But sometimes I wonder who will say,
On some far-distant witches' night,
"How about a pussy for the light?"

A PART OF THE MAIN

"An island you can never be
Alone in a gray and empty sea,"
Somewhere I read
That an old priest said,
And though he's dead,
He was talking to you and me.

Perhaps he talked to us in vain,
Since all his nameless and endless main,
To you and me,
Would seem to be
As the desolate sea,
And we would be lost again.

Yet I would be joined to humanity,
And so a peninsula I would be,
Where a green bough swings
And a sweet bird sings
And a sweet bell rings
In a place just for you and me.

SUNRISE

if day should come
only for those
who rose to worship
the morning stars
and dawn's first glow
behind the mountains
I fear our world
would be quite dim
but as it is
I feel compassion for
those north of us
and south of us
where it's still dark
while only here
across our land
rises the sun

I wish that I
might greet the sun
as Omar did
or Zarathustra
with a hymn
but if you see
your cosmologist
twice a year
he will assure you
that this great event
comes from the wobble
of a puny planet
upon its axis
as it drifts around
a minor star
sometimes I question
what we gain
when we trade wonder
for perspective

31

NEW YEAR'S EVE

Our Lord was born, the old books say,
Even as the lifegiving sun,
Along about midwinter day,
Its journey back began to run—
But who then but a chosen few
Knew he was Lord or the year was new?

It took a while for the world to see
That someone special was born that day
Whose words would go far from Galilee
And that spring and summer were on their way—
With libations and merriment, what we cheer
Is the Epiphany of the year.

ON THE TWELFTH DAY

I loved mankind
enough to let
them do their thing
alas
they blew it
now what
do I do

GRACE

Harmony of the worlds,
Source of all life,
Help us to feel
The joy of our feasting
More in our being together
Than in the feast.
May the peace and love
Among us here
Reach out and touch
The hearts of others
Beyond these walls,
Beyond this day.

HYMN TO THE SUN

Greeting to thee,
Light of the morning,
Giver of life,
Warmth of the world!

Now as our earth
Faces to bless thee,
Cheer with thy light,
Heal with thy rays!

Now we can face
Night's starlit abyss,
Knowing we soon
Turn back to thee!

A GRACE FOR THANKSGIVING

Lord, whom we know
Only as one
We cannot know,
Only the mystery
Behind all that is,
May the blessings we count
And the bounty we share
And the joy of this day
Be not ours alone—
And if there's a way
To thank a mystery,
Please let us know.

RESPONSIVE READING

1) WE CELEBRATE THE FACT OF OUR FELLOWSHIP,
   since we are part of humanity.

2) THEREFORE WE ARE PART OF EACH OTHER,
   but greater together than the
   sum of our parts.

3) WHEN WE COUNT OUR BLESSINGS TOGETHER,
   they are more than we could count
   by ourselves;

4) AND WHATEVER IS CREATIVE AND JOYFUL
   is only so when we share it.

5) WHEN WE THINK ABOUT WHO WE ARE,
   let us remember, too, who we're *of*.

II
A TRIP TO THE BLUE MOTEL

Remember when we went on the trip and we couldn't find where it was at?

—Carol (age 4)

One day Dolly and Pussy were sitting in the kitchen playing Monotony. Pussy said, "Dolly, playing Monotony gets awfully monotonous. Why don't we do something else for a change?"

"All right," said Dolly, "let's go on a trip up the highway and stay at a blue motel."

"Why must it be a blue one?" Pussy wanted to know.

"Because."

"Because what?"

"Because I said so," Dolly answered.

And that was that.

"I'll go fire up Marika," said Pussy, to change the subject. Marika was one of those nifty little imported ecological fire wagons that ran on recycled goat chow because she came from a country where they had lots of goats. Traveling around cattle and sheep country was kind of a problem, but Marika could run on recycled sheep chow if she had to; once, in fact, she even ran on recycled snake chow.

After she fired up Marika, Pussy got ready for the trip. Getting ready for a trip is a simple matter for a cat because all she needs is plenty of catnip. In fact, Pussy could have herself quite a trip just on the catnip, without any fire wagon at all; but on a catnip trip she couldn't take Dolly along, and that wouldn't be sociable.

Dolly, being a girl type doll, of course had to bring along all her worldly goods in a big brown paper sack. She didn't bring along a spare head like some dolls we know, but she brought along lots of barrettes and eye shadow and crayons and coloring books. (Sometimes you have to do a lot of traveling to find a blue motel.)

At last they were ready, and they piled the catnip and the sack of worldly goods into the back seat with ten sacks of goat chow and Nancybelle the goat. They had to have Nancybelle along to recycle the goat chow so Marika could burn it. Now that may sound a little complicated, but Marika was a *very* ecological fire wagon. In fact, she was made entirely of biodegradable materials so that if she broke down you could just leave her by the roadside and she would go back to nature all by herself.

So Marika puffed and chugged and choo-chooed and whooshed on up the highway. Now, stories for children still call trains on the

Union Pacific "choo-choos"; but they haven't choo-chooed since before you were born, which shows how much people who write children's stories know about the Union Pacific. But Marika was a genuine, honest-and-truly, bona fide ecological fire wagon; and she really did choo-choo when the going got tough. When the going wasn't tough, she just kind of whooshed, a nice, smooth, well-rounded ecological whoosh.

Well, Nancybelle was happily recycling goat chow for Marika, and Marika was happily whooshing along the highway, and Dolly was steering Marika, and Pussy was stoking her boiler, and everybody was enjoying the scenery, when they came to a brand inspector.

"I'm just a young brand inspector," he told them, "and I don't know much about this business yet; and if I thought you were Mr. Wenburg, I think I would just go and hide. But you don't look like you know what you're doing either; so I think that goat should have papers to cross the county line."

"But we're nowhere near the county line," Dolly protested.

"I know," said the brand inspector, "but at the rate you're going you're bound to come to one sooner or later." He turned to Nancybelle and said, "Let's see your papers." So Nancybelle showed him a *Branding Iron,* a *Boomerang,* a *Laramie Sentinel,* a *Unitarian-Universalist World,* and the bill of sale for the goat chow.

"I guess that's enough papers," the brand inspector agreed. "Those ought to get you into Carbon County and maybe even Sweetwater County if you sweet-talk that guy in Rock Springs."

"We're glad to know that," Pussy told him very graciously, "but we were just going to the Diamond Horseshoe to stay at a blue motel. But thanks, anyway."

So they whooshed on up the road and soon came to the Diamond Horseshoe, but they couldn't stay there because there weren't any blue motels. They were all pink and green. "Anyhow," Pussy said, "we might as well have lunch."

So Dolly and Pussy went into the restaurant to have lunch while Nancybelle stayed behind to catch up on her recycling, because it looked like it was going to be a long trip and maybe they *would* cross a county line before they got done. In fact, they might have to go all the way from Hither to Yon to find a blue motel.

Dolly was sitting up like a lady and eating her cheddar cheese soup because it was Friday, and Pussy was sitting up like a pussycat and sipping a catnip martooni because she *knew* it was going to be a long trip, when Dolly looked over at the next table and who do you think she saw? You'd never guess in a million years; so I'll just have to break down and tell you. She saw the road commissioner having lunch with one of his constituents! So she got up and went over to him and asked him (very politely, of course), "Excuse me, Mr. Road Commissioner; can you tell me how the road is from Hither to Yon?"

"I haven't been over it since I was elected," the road commissioner replied, "but maybe my constituent can help you."

"Well, young lady," said the constituent, "that road is all right, except you might have trouble getting through all the ditches."

The road commissioner was very surprised to hear this. "What happened to all the bridges over the ditches?" he wanted to know.

"Well," replied the constituent, "it seems like in the last seventy-five years they just kind of fell apart."

"In that case," said the road commissioner to Dolly, "your fire wagon won't do much whooshing. She'll have to choo-choo all the way. So when you get to Sweetwater County, be sure and sweet-talk that guy in Rock Springs."

"But we have to go through Carbon County to get there," Dolly reminded him. "Who can we sweet-talk in Carbon County?"

"The only one I know in Carbon County is the Virginian," the road commissioner answered, "and you'd better smile when you sweet-talk him."

"Oh, we will, we will," Dolly assured him. "In fact, Pussy just finished her martooni and she's smiling already." She thanked the road commissioner and his constituent for all their helpful information about the road from Hither to Yon and went back to her own table. "Pussy," she said, "you'd better go out and stoke up Marika real good, and tell Nancybelle to recycle the rest of the goat chow. It's going to be a long trip."

"Can I have another catnip martooni while Nancybelle is doing all that?" Pussy asked. Dolly looked askance at her friend (you haven't lived till you've seen a doll look askance). "OK," she said, still looking *very* askance, "but only one more." Just then the cocktail waitress eased by.

"Winnie! Bring me a double!" said Pussy.

Soon Marika was whooshing on up the highway again; but Dolly had to do most of the stoking herself, because Pussy was higher than a Chinese kite on catnip martoonis and wouldn't do anything but blink at the scenery. (Chinese kites fly higher than other kites, and I'll bet you didn't know *that* before.) Nancybelle spent most of the time snoozing, because she was very tired from recycling extra goat chow. So poor Dolly had to do *all* the work.

A little while after they went through Rock River, Pussy was beginning to pay attention to things once again; and she said to Dolly, "How do we find the road from Hither to Yon when we don't even know where Hither is?"

"Shut up and stoke," Dolly replied, somewhat ungraciously, since she was still a bit miffed at Pussy for getting high on catnip martoonis when there was work to do. Besides, Dolly didn't feel like letting on that she really didn't know where Hither was, either.

Not long after Pussy started stoking again they came to a hamlet. Do you know what a hamlet is? Well, it's a place kind of like Centennial, only smaller—more like Howell, I guess. Anyhow, that's what they came to; and Dolly backed off on the throttle and stepped on the brake and said, "Whoa, Marika." She really didn't have to say "Whoa," but Marika was a very sensitive fire wagon and appreciated having someone talk to her once in a while.

They had stopped in front of a café, because that's the best place to stop if you are looking for advice in a hamlet. And they were badly in need of advice. Pussy offered to go in and get the advice, but Dolly figured that she was just looking for a chance to have another catnip martooni; so Dolly went in herself. She asked the barmaid (very politely, of course), "How do we get to Hither?"

"Lady, you're in it," the barmaid replied.

"Oh. Then where is the road to Yon?" Dolly asked her, still very politely.

"Lady, you're on it," the barmaid replied.

"Oh. Where can I buy a few sacks of goat chow?" Dolly inquired then.

"Right here," the barmaid replied. "How many do you want?"

"Enough to get us to Yon," Dolly explained.

"It will take about eight sacks if you've got a good fire wagon. How efficient is your goat?"

Dolly assured her that Nancybelle was very efficient indeed. So she paid for the goat chow and started to leave, and Pussy stuck her head in the door and wanted to know where the post office was.

"Right here," the barmaid told her. So Pussy came in and mailed a letter she had written to her friends back in Howell about the big trip.

Just then a deputy sheriff came in and asked the barmaid for the key to the jail. Since the café was the only building they had seen since arriving in Hither, Pussy wanted to know where the jail was.

"Right here," the barmaid told her. Pussy decided that Hither was a very well organized hamlet indeed, since they had all the business in town under one roof—which would save a lot of steps in bad weather.

"I heard that the road from Hither to Yon is very rough," Dolly said to the barmaid. "Where does this fine highway end?"

"Right here," replied the barmaid; and indeed it did. You know how it is in Wyoming. You whoosh along a fine highway and you end up in some place like Hither. They looked up the road to where it petered out into a very rough-looking dirt road, and there was a sign that read, "TAKE THE SHORT CUT: ONLY 45 KILOMETERS FROM HITHER TO YON."

"Why is the distance in kilometers?" Pussy asked the barmaid.

"Well, the road commissioner heard that one of these days the U.S. will adopt the metric system, and he figured this would save him the trouble of changing the sign. Do you know how far 45 kilometers is? It's about 30 miles as the crow flies, if a crow could be persuaded to fly it.

"Good-bye, folks," the barmaid added, "don't forget to sweet-talk that guy in Rock Springs."

So they loaded up the eight sacks of goat chow and headed for Yon. It wasn't long before Marika was huffing and chugging and choo-chooing on that rough dirt road, instead of whooshing along as she had on the highway. "What a goat track!" exclaimed Pussy.

"Nyaaaaaaaaaaaah!" said Nancybelle, who didn't think that was a very nice thing to say about goats.

"Shut up and recycle," said Dolly most ungraciously. She was working very hard to keep Marika from drifting into the borrow pit.

And then they saw a blue motel! It was off to one side of the road, up on a hill. There was a sign by the driveway that looked like this:

```
U.S. BUREAU OF MINES
EXPERIMENTAL ALUMINUM
ORE  PROCESSING   PLANT

NO TRESPASSING
```

Now, Pussy was the only one on this trip who could read; so Dolly asked her (a little more graciously this time), "What does it say?"

Pussy studied the sign for a while, for she was a slow and careful reader, and finally replied, "It says 'NO VACANCIES.'" It was very disappointing, of course, after all that traveling to find a blue motel and then discover that they couldn't get in. But they kept choo-chooing over the rough road till they came to another café just like the one in Hither except that the sign read, "YON, WYOMING. POP. 11. ELEV. 7300." Since most places have more Pop. than Elev., they figured that Yon, Wyoming, must be quite a community, with all that Elev. and so little Pop. It was, too. Dolly and Pussy both went into the café this time. One of the Pop. was behind the bar, and the other ten were at the tables drinking their lunch.

"Tell me, Mr. Pop.," Pussy asked the bartender (very politely, of course), "where can we find a blue motel?"

"You'll have to sweet-talk that guy in Rock Springs," the bartender answered. Dolly decided that it was about time they found out why they needed to do this; so she asked the bartender, "Who is this guy in Rock Springs?"

"He's the one that owns the blue motel," the bartender informed her. "It's the only one in town. You can't miss it."

So they bought a few more sacks of goat chow and choo-chooed on down the road. Soon the rough road turned into a fine highway again, and Marika was able to whoosh along very ecologically; and the next thing they knew, they were in Rock Springs. It wasn't hard to find the only blue motel in town; and after they sweet-talked the owner, he fixed them up with lovely rooms and even a comfortable garage for Marika.

After they were snug in their beds and about to drift off into dreamland, Pussy said, "Dolly, I practiced my best smile all the way from Hither to Yon, and we never did see the Virginian."

"Go to sleep, pussycat," said Dolly, really quite graciously this time. "We'll sweet-talk him on the way home."

"Dolly," said Pussy again, for she was not yet quite asleep, "what's so great about staying in a blue motel?"

"Nothing, really," Dolly replied, "but look at the trip we had. It sure beat playing Monotony, now, didn't it?"

But Pussy was already asleep.

Notes

THE BLUE MOTEL: This story was inspired by an actual trip (which lasted about an hour) which my daughter and I took around the Laramie countryside. She was four years old at the time. The blue motel was her idea.

MARIKA (pronounced Ma-REEK-a): During my prep school days I became enchanted with a Greek actress by this name. This passion (of which, alas, the lady knew nothing) has since cooled, but I still like the name.

A FIRE WAGON: I spent several of my early years in steam automotive development work, and I still think there is a case for steam power on the highway. An "ecological fire wagon," that is, a steam-powered vehicle burning nonpolluting fuel, is a real possibility—even though it might not burn anything quite as exotic as the fuel for Marika.

.

III
PURRS AND SCRATCHES

IS RELIGION STILL POSSIBLE?

Religion essentially is the belief that the management of the universe is in hands other than our own, that some power above and beyond ourselves is running the show. Science has forced us to revise our notions about what this power is like. God as Jehovah, or even as our father in heaven, is indeed dead. Twentieth-century adults can no more believe in him than in Santa Claus.

This does not necessarily mean that God does not exist; it may mean only that his nature must be other than we had thought. Science has expanded the frontiers of empirical knowledge, which is the only kind most of us take much stock in today. But the very act of pushing back the frontiers brings home the fact that they are there. The old certainties have died, too. We have begun to learn how limited man's knowledge really is. Science, strangely enough, has given us back the unknown—and the unknowable. It has forced us to accept the fact of mystery, the fact that beyond the frontiers is much that we do not and probably cannot know.

We do not know why electrons as well as planets move in orbits and in orderly relationships to each other instead of whizzing hither and yon like flies in a kitchen. We do not know whence comes the essential harmony in the scheme of things that makes possible life. We do not and probably never will understand the ultimate mystery that makes our universe a cosmos instead of a chaos and is responsible for the very fact that we're here.

If this mystery moves you to reverence, to a sense of communion with the scheme of things, a sense of sharing with your fellow men in the adventure of life, then you have a religion, and it is not incompatible with the state of man's knowledge. Most of the doctrinal differences that produced such a bewildering variety of churches are no longer meaningful. But this does not mean that religion can no longer be meaningful.

Has God really died? Or has he merely updated his image? Are the teachings of Jesus of any less value if Jesus, like Socrates, Lao-tse, Dag Hammarskjold, or Martin Buber, turns out to be human? If there is no Santa Claus and there is no pie in the sky, what of that?

The sky is still there.

AS THE YEAR TURNS

I have always felt that our Jewish friends celebrate their New Year much better than we do ours. For them the turning of the year is a high and solemn time, a time for prayer and rededication. What is it that we Gentiles celebrate with our New Year's Eve whoopee? That we have somehow stumbled through one more year and the time has come to let down our hair before picking up the burden again? Would people rededicating themselves with fresh resolve and high hope comport themselves thus?

Here among our prairies and mountains we still know the seasons. The birthday of Jesus is also the time when we know for sure that the sun is on its way back to us to quicken the earth with new life, to set the mountain streams to running again, and to make the hillsides and meadows green again. I don't think our kind of New Year's Eve originated in Wyoming, or in ancient Palestine either. It must be the creation of city dwellers, who know little of growing things, who rarely see the sun and do not feel the good earth. That a cycle has been fulfilled in the growth of living things and another cycle begun with new promise is the real meaning of the new year, and it is sad that the inhabitants of our great Gomorrahs and megalopolises have so little contact with this. For them, the calendar simply runs out and one must hang up a new one.

As we grow older, the turning of the year reminds us of how swiftly time passes, and we think how precious time is and wonder if, in the year now gone, we have spent it well. Will we do better in the year now beginning? What of value can we create and pass on, and will we have time?

I think we feel that the beginning of a new cycle of seasons is cause for celebration because, in a very real way, we feel that we have a fresh chance. A year ends, and the next begins. But it is not just the next, not just another, not just a repetition of the year we've been through. It is a *new* year, with new promise, new hope, and new challenges.

Rejoice in its coming. It's for you.

WE ARE RISEN

Why do we celebrate Easter? I doubt if very many of our faith believe that Jesus or anyone else ever literally arose from the dead. For that matter, strangely enough, all four Gospels dismiss this spectacular event with a brief chapter or two; and after the resurrection, Jesus does not seem to have done anything nearly as remarkable as he had before it. To go by the scriptures, the inspiration for the most joyful and holy day of our year seems to have been something of an anticlimax.

Yet the celebration of Easter *is* meaningful to us. It is meaningful because our roots are Christian. It is meaningful because we value our traditions and cherish our heritage. It is meaningful because it honors the memory of a brave and compassionate man whose teachings, for all the change in the world since his time, still guide and inspire us. And it is meaningful to us in its old pagan sense, too, as a celebration of the renewal of life with the coming of spring.

It is perhaps mostly in this last sense that Easter is still important as a festival of our faith. When we took our legends more literally, we began this day with the joyful shout, "He is risen!"—a cry that rings oddly to our ears in the current Year of Our Lord. But can we not still renew our spirits at the wellspring of his teaching? And what better time to renew our communion with all life than the return of the sun and the beginning of spring? How better can we honor the memory of Jesus than by being able to say, truthfully and from our hearts—"*We* are risen!"

THE GOSPEL OF NICODEMUS

I believe in God the Father Almighty, maker of heaven and earth: and in Jesus Christ his only son, our Lord: Who was conceived by the Holy Ghost, born of the Virgin Mary, Suffered under Pontius Pilate, was crucified, dead, and buried; He descended into hell. . . .

—The Apostles' Creed
Book of Common Prayer

Since we find meaning and inspiration in many faiths, it is not surprising that our Fellowship should sometimes celebrate the Christian Easter and also, as we did last Sunday, the Jewish Passover. It is interesting that the Jewish festivals celebrate events in the history of a whole people, while the Christian festivals celebrate events in the life of one man. Some of the more interesting events in the story of that man are not even told in the Gospels.

I once remarked upon the strange fact that the astonishing miracle of Christ's resurrection, which has only lately been duplicated on a small scale by medical science, is only briefly mentioned in the canonical Gospels. Though it is celebrated by the most solemn rites in the Christian calendar, the event itself is tacked onto the first three Gospels almost as a footnote, and John's Gospel is nearly as sketchy. In the articles of faith known as the Apostles' Creed, there is the curious assertion that Jesus descended into hell, a part of the story that we do not find in the Bible at all.*

How Jesus descended into hell and what he did there and the other events that occurred after his resurrection are, however, recounted in the apocryphal Gospel of Nicodemus. Nicodemus appears in the Gospel of John, where he is mentioned as a Pharisee who was friendly to Jesus, tried to defend him before Pontius Pilate, and supplied the materials for embalming the body after his death.

It is inevitable that a body of legend should grow up around the personality of someone who influenced the minds and hearts of men as profoundly as Jesus did, and early Christian folklore is just as enjoyable as that about such later figures as Saint Patrick or

---

* There is, however, a rather vague reference in Paul's letter to the Ephesians (Eph. 4:8-9).

Abraham Lincoln. The Gospel of Nicodemus is an engaging document, and it's too bad it was left out of the Bible. According to Nicodemus, the hell into which Jesus descended after his resurrection was not the fiery pit of eternal damnation that it later became in fundamentalist doctrine, but was more like the Greek Hades, the underworld where dwelt the spirits of the dead. Beelzebub, the prince of hell, seems to have presided over this establishment much like the Roman Pluto.

Residing in hell were Adam, Isaiah, John the Baptist, King David, and all the prophets and patriarchs except Elijah and Enoch, who had made it directly to heaven. Jesus descended into hell, broke down the gates, and released Adam and the patriarchs and prophets and led them by the hand up to heaven. Satan had tried to warn Beelzebub against letting Christ enter into hell, and they quarreled bitterly. After Jesus freed all the saints and broke Beelzebub's power, Satan said, "I told you so"; and Beelzebub in turn accused Satan of getting him into this mess by allowing the crucifixion to happen.

> While the prince of hell was thus speaking to Satan, the King
> of Glory said to Beelzebub, the prince of hell: "Satan the prince
> shall be subject to thy dominion for ever, in the room of Adam
> and his righteous sons, who are mine." (Nicodemus 18:14)

So Jesus let Beelzebub have Satan in exchange for Adam and all the saints and prophets and patriarchs. I'm sure that Beelzebub felt that he got the short end of the deal.

The fact that at least sometimes he still does is the reason we celebrate Easter.

Note: The Gospel of Nicodemus may be found in *The Lost Books of the Bible and the Forgotten Books of Eden* (Cleveland: World Publishing Company, 1926, 1927).

WHAT IT'S ABOUT

We all know the Christmas story: the miraculous child born to a virgin and cradled in a manger nearly 2,000 Christmases ago because there was no room in the inn; the pilgrimage of the wise men to do him honor; and the choirs of angels appearing to the shepherds to herald their savior. We know, too, the story of the miracles, the teachings, the final betrayal, and the tragic death of the young man around whose legend Paul built his church.

Soon we shall once again celebrate the anniversary of Jesus's birth. But in this post-Christian, postindustrial, and perhaps post-human world, though we still sing the old carols, what, to us today, does Christmas actually mean?

There is, of course, the tawdry commercialism, the orgy of extravagance to sate the greed of spoiled children, and in every store good old Santa, the patron saint of it all, making his pitch to the kiddies. The saccharine strains of "Rudolph the Red-Nosed Reindeer" and "White Christmas" blare from loudspeakers in every block until even Jesus would be hard put to forgive their composers. If Scrooge said "Bah!" to this, I'm with him. But is it really for this shabby Saturnalia of free enterprise that we still observe Christmas?

It may seem that way, but I think that not only Christmas, but our civilization along with it, would long since have perished if people were really as bad as all that. The old religious meanings have blurred to where Jews observe Christmas and Unitarian-Universalists celebrate Hanukkah, but the human meanings are the same all over the world. This is the time of year when the rat race slows down, the human scene takes on a kindlier glow, and whatever there may be within us of the bestowing virtue comes a little closer to the surface. This is the time when we show with our gifts that we love one another.

To bring pleasure to someone you care about, and even to someone you may not care about, is perhaps the most enjoyable thing a human being can do. We can't be all bad so long as we set aside a special time of the year just for this.

Why do we pick the birthday of Jesus? "I love you," he said, "just as the Father loves me. Remain in my love."

And that's what it's all about.

THE PROTEVANGELION

I have known the traditional story of the birth of Jesus—the story we celebrate in our Christmas carols—ever since I can remember. But I grew up in suburbia; so I never knew what a manger was. In fact, I never heard anybody use the word until I moved to Wyoming, where it seems to mean just what *Webster's Third* says it does: "A trough or open box in which feed or fodder is placed for horses or cattle to eat."

For the details of our Christmas story we depend entirely on the Gospel of Luke. Matthew says only that Jesus was born in Bethlehem and that wise men from the east followed a star to the place where he was. The Gospels of Mark and John give no account of his birth, but begin with his first encounter with John the Baptist.

Something else used to puzzle me: Why is Christ referred to as "Jesus of Nazareth" when he was born in Bethlehem? Nazareth, a town midway between the southern end of the large freshwater lake that we call the Sea of Galilee and the Mediterranean coast, was where his family lived. (Palestine at that time was a Roman province which enjoyed a good deal of autonomy with respect to its internal affairs and still had its own king, at that time, Herod.)

Augustus Caesar had decreed that all the people of the province must report to their tribal headquarters to be registered in the imperial census. For Joseph and his family, this meant traveling to Bethlehem, seat of the house of David, to which Joseph belonged. Bethlehem is about five miles south of Jerusalem, about seventy miles south of Nazareth, and about fifteen miles west of the northern end of the Dead Sea. In those days, for the family of a poor carpenter, this was a considerable journey and probably took several days. Mary, in the last month of her pregnancy, was allowed to ride the family donkey, but the rest of the family probably walked. According to the Protevangelion, an apocryphal Gospel attributed to Christ's brother James (who later became head of the Christian community in Jerusalem), they didn't quite make it before the baby arrived.

The Protevangelion intrigues me because many of the early church fathers considered it to be as authentic as the canonical Gospels; and it is the only one besides Luke's which goes into any detail about the circumstances of Christ's birth. Furthermore, its story is quite different from Luke's. James (if indeed he was the author) says that Mary went into labor about three miles outside of Bethlehem and asked Joseph to take her down from the donkey:

But Joseph replied, Whither shall I take thee? for the place is desert.

Then said Mary again to Joseph, Take me down, for that which is within me mightily presses me.

And Joseph took her down.

And he found there a cave, and let her into it. (Prot. 12:11-14)

And leaving her and his sons in the cave, Joseph went forth to seek a Hebrew midwife in the village of Bethlehem. (Prot. 13:1)

And the midwife went along with him, and stood in the cave.

Then a bright cloud overshadowed the cave, and the midwife said, This day my soul is magnified, for mine eyes have seen surprising things, and salvation is brought forth to Israel.

But on a sudden the cloud became a great light in the cave, so that their eyes could not bear it.

But the light gradually decreased, until the infant appeared, and sucked the breast of Mary.

Then the midwife cried out, and said, How glorious a day this is, wherein mine eyes have seen this extraordinary sight! (Prot. 14:9-13)

So the wise men went forth, and behold, the star which they saw in the east went before them, till it came and stood over the cave where the young child was with Mary his mother. (Prot. 15:9)

King Herod, feeling his throne threatened by the birth of one whom the Jews hailed as their king, ordered his hatchet men to kill all infants under the age of two years, but Joseph and his family got wind of this plot:

But Mary, hearing that the children were to be killed, being under much fear, took the child and wrapped him up in swaddling clothes, and laid him in an ox-manger, because there was no room for them in the inn. (Prot. 16:2)

That's as far as the Protevangelion goes with the story of Jesus. The remainder of the Gospel is about the escape of Elizabeth with her son John (the John who later baptized Jesus) and the murder of her husband, Zacharias the priest.

What if, on the strength of new discoveries in biblical archaeology, the churches should decide to canonize the Protevangelion and relegate Luke to the Apocrypha? What would happen to all our fine old Christmas carols about the little town of Bethlehem and the herald angels singing to the shepherds?

Something tells me we'd go right on singing them. What really matters to us, and what I'm sure mattered most to both Luke and James, is not that Jesus was born in a cave or a stable, but that he was born.

Note: The quotations from the Protevangelion were taken from *The Lost Books of the Bible and the Forgotten Books of Eden* (Cleveland: World Publishing Company, 1926, 1927).

FLIGHT INTO EGYPT

We remember how Joseph, as the result of the jealousy of his brothers, was sold into slavery in Egypt and how he later found favor with the Pharaoh and became his right-hand man. In gratitude for Joseph's saving Egypt from famine, Pharaoh invited Joseph's family to settle in the Land of Goshen, a choice section of the Nile delta. A later Pharaoh, alarmed that their descendants had become a mighty people, enslaved and oppressed them until Moses led them back to their ancestral home in the land of Canaan. The Jewish Passover celebrates their deliverance from Egypt, and the Egyptians of biblical times are remembered more for their role as oppressors than for their earlier hospitality to the Jews or their many later instances of hospitality to them and alliance with them in war.

When Joseph's great-grandfather Abram first settled in Canaan, there was a famine in the land and he and Sarai went down to Egypt, where they were hospitably received, and whence Abram returned a rich man. When Sarai proved barren, Abram had a son Ishmael by her Egyptian maid, Hagar (though when Sarai finally bore a son of her own, she drove Hagar and Ishmael out of the house).

When Solomon learned that Jeroboam was a threat to his throne, "Solomon sought therefore to kill Jeroboam; but Jeroboam arose, and fled into Egypt, to Shishak king of Egypt until the death of Solomon" (1 Kings 11:40).

When King Sennacherib of Assyria invaded Judah, one of his generals taunted King Hezekiah for his reliance on Egypt: "On what do you rest this confidence of yours? . . . Behold, you are relying now on Egypt, that broken reed of a staff, which will pierce the hand of any man who leans on it" (2 Kings 18:19, 21). Isaiah also took a dim view of reliance on Egypt: " 'Woe to the rebellious children,' says the Lord, '. . . who set out to go down to Egypt, without asking for my counsel, to take refuge in the protection of Pharaoh, and to seek shelter in the shadow of Egypt!' " (Isa. 30:1-2).

During the last years of the Kingdom of Judah, before its conquest by the Babylonians who carried off the whole population and kept them as slaves for seventy years, many Jews took refuge in Egypt, to the consternation of the Prophet Jeremiah: "And what do you gain by going to Egypt, to drink the water of the Nile?" (Jer. 2:18). And again he says, "Do not fear the king of Babylon, of whom you are afraid; do not fear him, says the Lord. . . . But if you say, 'We will not remain in this land,' disobeying the voice of the Lord your God and saying, 'No, we will go to the land of Egypt, where we shall not see war, or hear the sound of the trumpet, or be hungry for bread, and we will dwell there . . .' " (Jer. 42:13-14). Nonetheless, many ignored Jeremiah and did flee to Egypt: "When Jeremiah finished speaking . . . all the insolent men said to Jeremiah, 'You are telling a lie. The Lord our God did not send you to say, "Do not go to Egypt to live there." ' So Johanan the son of Kareah and all the commanders of the forces and all the people did not obey the voice of the Lord, to remain in the land of Judah. . . . And they came into the land of Egypt, for they did not obey the voice of the Lord" (Jer. 43:1-2, 4, 7).

This flight into Egypt would seem to have been a sensible move under the circumstances, but Jeremiah stuck to his guns and told the refugees that they would live to regret it: "Therefore thus says the Lord of hosts, the God of Israel . . . 'I will take the remnant of Judah who have set their faces to come to the land of Egypt to live, and they shall all be consumed; in the land of Egypt they shall fall; . . . I will punish those who dwell in the land of Egypt, as I have punished Jerusalem, with the sword, and with famine, and with pestilence, so that none of the remnant of Judah who have come to live in the land of Egypt shall escape or survive or return to the land of Judah' " (Jer. 44:11-14).

Like Isaiah, Jeremiah had no faith in the alliance with Egypt: "Then the word of the Lord came to Jeremiah the prophet: '. . . Behold, Pharaoh's army which came to help you is about to return to Egypt, to its own land. And the Chaldeans shall come back and fight against this city; they shall take it and burn it with fire' " (Jer. 37:7-8). Which, as we all know, they did.

Even in New Testament times, Egypt retains her status as a refuge for losers from the land of Canaan. When Jesus was born, King Herod was determined that his infant rival should not survive. "Now when they [the wise men from the east] had departed, an angel of the Lord appeared to Joseph in a dream and said, 'Rise, take the child and his mother, and flee to Egypt, and remain there till I tell you;

63

for Herod is about to search for the child, to destroy him.' And he rose and took the child and his mother by night, and departed to Egypt, and remained there until the death of Herod" (Matt. 2:13-15). (This episode also occurs in the apocryphal Protevangelion. Mark, Luke, and John make no mention of it.)

Except when the Jews wore out their welcome by becoming too numerous in her land, Egypt seems to have been the country that the Jews, kings and commoners alike, always turned to in time of trouble.

Note: The quotations are from the Revised Standard Version of the Bible.

A NEW YEAR

The calendar helps us to mark the passage of time and keep our records straight. But why do we take such pains, with our Gregorian revisions and leap years, to keep it in step with the sun and the moon? What bearing need the phases of the moon or the signs of the zodiac have on when we start school or pay the telephone bill? What have sunrise and sunset to do with the lives of those who work by artificial light in air-conditioned buildings and begin and end their days by the clock?

Not much, it would seem; but artificial as it often may be, human life is still life—and all life came from the sea. The rhythm of the tides still flows in our veins, and the cycle of the seasons—of rebirth and renewal, growth and fulfillment, planting and cultivating and harvest—is the cycle of all human life.

What is more natural than that we should base our calendars on the motions of the moon and the sun? That there is a sun to give life to our world and that this world journeys around it in a harmonious and infallible way is the one supreme fact of our very existence. One could do worse than worship the sun, and some peoples have.

Were the universe a chaos instead of a cosmos, we could not be. There is a scheme of things that makes us possible, and astrology can't be all bad if, for all its fantastical nonsense, it does teach us this. Our calendar is not a mere timekeeper's schedule. The lunar and solar cycles that it symbolizes are those of our lives. It is fitting that we celebrate the New Year, for it is both a cosmic and a human event. It is the beginning of a new cycle for the earth, the moon, the sun, and ourselves.

Happy New Year! For we and the cosmos are one.

OUT OF PHASE?

Not many people will dispute the truism that we could make a paradise of this earth simply by channeling our energy and our wealth into projects for improving man's lot instead of into the means for annihilating the species. The question is, Why don't we?

I have an idea that when a society's technology is in phase with its culture, it has a good thing going, as the ancient Greeks did. When either gets ahead of the other, the society is in trouble. In the Orient we have seen societies with an advanced culture but a backward technology fall into desperate straits, as India has, or into Communist hands, as China has. Here in the West we have created our own kind of desperation by letting our technology outstrip our culture. Our ways of thinking about our society and our world are at least a century behind what our science has made it possible for us to make of it.

Our culture—our philosophy, our arts, our ethics, our politics, and our religion—needs to catch up with our science. Until we get in phase with ourselves, we will be in as bad a fix as the countries whose science hasn't caught up with their culture.

TOWARD HUMANITY

The complexity of human society has caused man to feel the need of a higher authority than himself. His religions, his governments, and his laws represent his attempts to provide it; but even the noblest of human creations is still a human creation, and therein is our weakness. Our deities are still anthropomorphic, and our supreme courts are still just groups of old men. There is no such thing as "a government of laws, not men"; a government of laws, which are enacted, interpreted, and enforced by human beings, is nothing *but* a government of men.

Man has yet to create any institution superior to himself; in fact, the moral of some of our science fiction seems to be that he would be in worse trouble than he is now if he could. There *is* a point to the hippie communes and other simplistic social experiments. A society simple enough to get by with just man himself and no "higher" institutions as fallible as their creators might be a backward step, but not an altogether unattractive one.

Man's hope, however, does not lie in what he can make of his world, but in what he can make of himself. Philip Wylie once said that to have a better world we must become better people. Nietzche said the same thing, and in *The Greening of America*, Reich says it, too.

"Man is something to be surpassed. What have ye done to surpass man?" said Zarathustra; and again he said, "But pray tell me, my brethren, if the goal of humanity be still lacking, is there not also still lacking—humanity itself?"

Can we create humanity—before it's too late?

WAVE OF THE FUTURE?

The hippies of the sixties were an inferior breed compared to the beatniks of an earlier decade. Where the beatniks were zestful and positive, the hippies were nihilistic, parasitic, and negative. The beatniks dug the American scene; the hippies rejected it. To be sure, the beatniks were bohemians and eccentrics; but at least they were mature and they created some literature of permanent value. The hippies don't seem to have created much of anything.

The "counterculture" challenged values that needed challenging, but (*The Greening of America* notwithstanding) it had no blueprint for a counterestablishment capable of running a complex modern society. Someone must still do the work, and what plans had they for this? The best they achieved was a few futile communes, which are nothing new in American history. For most Americans, this kind of pastoral primitivism is not an acceptable answer.

The counterculture was a sort of antielite that only an affluent society could afford. If they could live on peace and love it was because somebody, somewhere, was still doing the work.

THOUGHTS AND SAYINGS

Tyranny is never illegal.

*   *   *

Self-expression is fine for children with finger paints; but if a grown man has nothing to express but himself, he is no artist.

*   *   *

That the laws of economics are immutable, like the laws of physics, is nonsense. Economics is a man-made thing, and what man can make he can unmake.

*   *   *

It is not such a comfort to the world as we would like to think it is, that we oppose communism. So did Hitler.

*   *   *

The fact that people die for their countries is an excellent argument for not having countries.

*   *   *

I don't think that a "lack of communication" is at the root of our troubles. What we suffer from is not a lack, but a glut. These days *everybody* communicates. The trouble is that we have nothing of any value to say.

*   *   *

We lost the American dream when we sold our libertarian birthright for a mess of imperialist pottage. The process began when we replaced the Articles of Confederation, with their clear-cut safeguards against the abuses of centralized power, with a Constitution so weasel-worded that the Supreme Court must work full time just to interpret it.

*   *   *

It is interesting that all our national holiday celebrates is a document: not the achievement of independence at all, but merely its assertion on paper. Independence did not become a fact for another six years, during which we had to fight one of the grimmest wars in our history for it.

* * *

If our affairs are being so criminally mismanaged that we must prepare for nuclear warfare, then the first thing we had better do is change managers.

* * *

Patriotism is love of one's homeland, not loyalty to a government. The great patriots have been the great revolutionists.

* * *

As the only nation ever to use atomic weapons on people, we have done a certain amout of breast-beating and soul-searching about Hiroshima. We have even made the excuse that it shortened the war or saved American lives, though Japan was already defeated. But we are strangely silent about Nagasaki, for what reason had we to do this awful thing *twice?*

* * *

Probably the only effect of financial disclosure laws will be to keep a lot of good people out of politics. We want to attract better people to public service, but we won't do it by invading their privacy and harassing them with discriminatory laws.

* * *

Where other cultures regard childhood as an apprenticeship to adulthood, we tend to concern ourselves too much with children as such. Real life calls for responsible adults, not overgrown kids. The only really useful thing a kid can do is grow up, and that is what we should encourage and help him to do.

* * *

We are spending public money to show the Chicano housewife how to cook more nourishing meals, when what the poor woman probably needs is a chance to get out of the kitchen.

* * *

We pontificate about "making a better world for our grand-children" when we can't even make a decent world for ourselves. If we could, maybe the kids would have a decent world to inherit.

* * *

I do not think that "sensitivity" is everyone's bag, since not all of us are intellectual or spiritual nudists. I have no more business poking around in your psyche than I have poking around in your house. I prefer to respect your privacy as I hope you will respect mine. There is not necessarily any special virtue in knowing one another too well, and it often does more harm than good.

* * *

There is no such thing as negotiating from a position of strength. When you are in a position of strength, you don't need to negotiate.

* * *

I am wondering if the grape and lettuce boycotters are really going to help the working man by threatening to put his employer out of business. If they fail, the employee will still have a crummy job; if they succeed, he will have no job at all.

"But Martin Luther King was not murdered by one man. He was assassinated by all the people of this nation." I quote this from *Paideia,* a campus "underground" paper that flourished for a season in the late sixties at the University of Wyoming. It's quite a statement. Even Russia in her wildest days never got as collectivist as all that. There are millions of reasonable, decent, fair-minded people in this country who have never harmed or insulted members of any minority group, nor would they want to. You might enlist their help—but you won't do it by accusing them of crimes they never committed.

This beating of the collective breast, this sloppy socializing of guilt, might be good for your soul; but just how much good do you think it is doing anyone else? To say that the people of Rock Springs or Greybull caused the problems of Harlem or Watts is patently silly; but it is a lot easier than the dedication, the serious study, and the hard work you would need to understand what really has caused those problems and to do something constructive about them.

I get a little tired of suburban liberals who come out to Wyoming and harangue us about ghettos. Back in the thirties Americans who felt deeply concerned about the issues involved in the Spanish Civil War went over to Spain and fought in it. If you are that deeply concerned about the problems of the inner city, perhaps the first thing you should do is go live there. "New York City can only be saved by the people who live here and care about it," said Donald Szantho Harrington, minister of New York's famous Community Church. After all, Hiroshima these days is a pretty nice town. . . .

Along with the notion that the world is a global village seems to go the notion that we've got to run it, despite the fact that most of the inhabitants object rather strongly and that the notion of a village of three billion people is an utterly preposterous one in the first place. A hundred causes clamor for our involvement, but the average citizen, with responsibilities to his own family and his own work, is rarely able to get involved effectively in more than two or three of them. The pitch for one charity does say, "We aren't trying to save the world, just one little corner of it"; and that's about all that most of us can be expected to do.

To be involved with something bigger and better than your own everyday life, to be concerned for your fellow man—this is a great way to be. But the poor devil who lets himself worry about everything and everybody in the whole world and allows himself to be pressured into involvement with every cause that comes down the pike will *not* be a happy and fulfilled individual. He will be a futile, depressed, and frustrated one, possibly to the point of suicide (and, you preachers of "involvement," don't think *that* hasn't happened!).

Think of the great benefactors of mankind: Buddha, Jesus, Servetus, Schweitzer, Tom Dooley, Tom Edison, Tom Paine, Gandhi, for a few. Did they go in for "sensitivity" and "involvement"? It seems rather that they stuck to their chosen work; they were doing their thing. Their lives were supremely devoted to one particular cause that they cared about very deeply. Happy is he who can find his cause and devote himself to it.

EXPERTS ALL

Lin Yutang once said that there are two kinds of philosophers: the kind who make difficult things simple, and the kind who make simple things difficult. A great many of our activities seem to be inspired by the latter, and I often wonder why we go to such pains to be so technical and complex about simple things.

Take the automobile, a mechanical contrivance designed to carry people from one place to another, having the great advantage of being personally owned transportation that enables one to go where he wants at his own convenience. Now look what we've made of it—a palatial carriage, a symbol of social status, a home on wheels, a kind of sport, a vast industry! Many people today live more in their cars than in their homes, and the number of people whose entire lives revolve around this conveyance runs into the millions. Our economy is largely based on the production of these vehicles, and a strike in Detroit is a national calamity—all this despite the fact that people got around just fine before the darn thing was even invented (the entire United States was settled without it!), and the cessation of automobile production for five years during the forties didn't hurt the country a bit.

Or skiing. When I was a kid it was great fun to slide down a snow covered hill on a couple of wooden runners strapped to the feet—which is all skiing is. And now we have ski resorts, ski schools (!) and highly paid engineers just designing the gear. A children's pastime has been blown up into an Olympic sport and a major industry. The simple fun I had as a boy would be out of the question today. I couldn't even qualify as a ski bum. I wouldn't even be allowed on the slopes. The professionals have long since taken over.

Or baseball. We kids used to get the gang together and head for a vacant lot and play ball. Today, the grown-ups have taken charge. To play ball now, a kid must register for Little League (do they take his fingerprints, too?) and con his folks into underwriting a uniform. It's all regimented and organized now—not, I suspect, for the benefit of the kids, who always played baseball anyway, but so that Daddy could play manager and feel public-spirited and important.

And cooking! There must be literally hundreds of cookbooks on the market, gourmet and otherwise, despite the fact that cooking is really a very simple affair. I can produce enjoyable meals—and frequently do—and I've probably consulted a cookbook about three times in my life. I very rarely even measure ingredients—not that I'm any genius, but cooking just is not that precise a business. Yet we spend millions of dollars to be told that it is.

And what of bowling? It used to be played by simple folk on the village green with about $5 worth of equipment. Now it has been technologized and professionalized to where one professional bowler earned over $85,000 in a single year!

And how about fishing? Any kid can tie a string to a stick and a hook to the string and catch as many fish as anyone else; yet fishing is one of our more technical sports. Millions of dollars are made by the companies who provide its aficionados with fancy equipment. Every fisherman has his own theories, and every fisherman is an expert.

And here, I think, is the key. Actually, almost anyone can drive a car, slide down a hill, play baseball, cook dinner, roll a large ball across a hardwood floor, or catch fish. But by complicating these simple activities, developing a technology and a mystique about them, we give ourselves a chance to play expert.

LA DIFFÉRENCE

Women need equality with men, not equivalence to them. They can do just about anything as well as men can, but will not necessarily do it in the same way. Therein may lie our best hope. As a man's world, our old earth has got into pretty much of a mess.

It is precisely because women *are* different that when they come into their own as complete human beings, we can look forward to a more humane world.

Read Susanne Langer's *Philosophy in a New Key,* the poems of Anne Sexton, Margaret Widdemer, or Edna Millay, the essays of Joan Didion and Mary McCarthy, or Zenna Henderson's poignant science fiction tale, *Pilgrimage,* and ask yourself what man could have created these works.

If that doesn't open your eyes, try Elaine Morgan's *The Descent of Woman.* Evolutionwise, it puts Man the Mighty Hunter in his place; and maybe it's about time.

SCIENCE FICTION BY WOMEN

I have enjoyed science fiction ever since I read Eric Frank Russell's *Sinister Barrier* in the March 1939 issue of *Unknown*—a copy of which I still cherish. In the early seventies, while I was still teaching linguistics at the University of Wyoming, I lectured to a discussion group (composed mainly of faculty members and other campus intellectuals) on the subject, "Science Fiction as Literature." I tried to show that science fiction is a bona fide literary genre worthy of the serious attention of scholars despite the contrary opinions of such prestigious critics as Leslie Fiedler, to say nothing of some of my audience.

Though a woman, Mary Shelley, may well be said to have originated the genre with *Frankenstein;* though fiction in general (including, interestingly enough, the detective story) has been a field in which women authors have always held their own; and though the women's liberation movement is encouraging more and more women to realize their full potential in fields long exclusively male, I am struck by the fact that even now so few science fiction authors are women. The 10 collections of SF short stories in my library, containing a total of 143 stories, contain exactly 7 stories by women—5 of them in a single collection of 13 French SF stories (which may or may not prove something about France). Of about 135 full-length SF novels in my library, exactly 4 are by women. Women, then, wrote about 3 percent of all the full-length SF novels and about 6 percent of the short stories in what can hardly be called a complete library of the genre but may fairly be considered a representative one.

I do not presume to explain why this is, except that women science fiction writers may be rare for the same reasons (whatever they are) that women scientists are rare. What intrigues me is their work. How, if at all, does science fiction written by women differ from that written by men?

The five French SF stories by women, referred to above, are closer to the type of fantasy found in Roald Dahl's short stories or Rod Serling's "Twilight Zone" tales than to science fiction proper. This is also true of Jessamyn West's novel, *The Chilekings,* in which all adults become miniaturized overnight to the size of Barbie dolls and the children take over. This is not really science fiction, since no explanation is given of how or why this transformation takes place—it just happens, like the separate masculine and feminine worlds of Philip Wylie's *The Disappearance.*

Two of the four full-length SF novels I have by women are written in the first person: *The Chilekings,* and Margaret St. Clair's *The Dancers of Noyo* (the latter, incidentally, being what I would call true science fiction). What interests me here is that the narrator in both novels is a man. Male SF writers do have women in their stories; in fact, they have written some very moving love stories in the genre. But I do not recall any male SF author who writes in the first person with a woman as the narrator. Are women more sensitive to nuances of personality, and thus better able to identify with the opposite sex, than men are? On the basis of this admittedly slim evidence, it would seem so.

A science fiction author must not only create the characters who people his world; he must often create their world, too. What kind of worlds do women SF writers create? In *Dragonquest,* Anne McCaffrey has created a world fully as exotic as Frank Herbert's *Dune* or Isaac Asimov's *Foundation;* but for all its strangeness, her planet, Pern, is a gentle and thoroughly human world. The great, fierce "dragons" that inhabit it live in a loving symbiosis with their human riders. Among the latter there are occasional duels, but no wars, and the enemy that threatens to wipe out the planet is not human or even humanoid, but a mindless sort of spore that tries to invade Pern from another planet. Pern, with its strange life forms and the civilization that human colonists have evolved there, is merely the setting, the backdrop for what is really a drama of human struggles and human hearts.

The qualities of gentleness, intimacy, warmth, and affection are what appealed to me most about Zenna Henderson's *Pilgrimage,* and these qualities seem to shine more brightly in science fiction by women than in most science fiction by men. In the latter, by and large, we find a man's world; whereas in the former we find, not merely a woman's world, but a human one.

DON'T CALL ME AND I WON'T CALL YOU

A friend visiting an old Yankee farmer asked him why he let the phone ring without bothering to answer it. "I had that thing installed for *my* convenience," he replied. We tend to forget that people have telephones installed for their convenience, not ours or that of rug peddlers, insurance salesmen, or solicitors for charity drives. We forget that when we call someone up we are invading his privacy, interrupting what he is doing, and compelling him to talk when *we* want to instead of when he does.

I have never seen any statistics showing what percentage of telephone subscribers keep their numbers unlisted, since the telephone companies don't care to publicize the fact that many people dislike talking on the telephone and find needless phone calls annoying. No law requires you to have a telephone any more than it requires you to have a fireplace; yet we have been brainwashed into believing that we have to give our phone numbers to census takers, issuers of credit cards, and anyone else who demands them. Actually, *nobody* has any more right to your phone number than he has to a key to your house.

Why is it that people will spend two or three dollars to make a long-distance phone call when an ordinary letter only costs a few cents to send and is a much more considerate communication? The recipient of a letter can put it aside and read it at *his* convenience, and often he will enjoy rereading it two or three times.

Many people still associate long-distance calls with tragedies and emergencies—I know I do—so the first thing your call probably does for your party is alarm him. When you call someone up in the middle of his dinner or his favorite TV program or while he's working on his income tax, "just to say hello" or to play organ music to him, he will probably be more exasperated than pleased. I have seen utterly trivial long-distance phone calls disrupt my whole household to the point where I was ready to have the phone taken out. One of my relatives called me from half a continent away just to tell me he might be passing through Laramie the following summer —a message he could just as well have put on a postcard. An old buddy equally faraway called up just because he was drinking a little wine and felt like calling people up. Well, I wasn't drinking wine, I was trying to work, and I did not appreciate being called up.

Writing letters seems to be out of fashion today. I don't think people fail to write letters because they are too busy, but because they are lazy. Certainly, when we've got almost the whole population taking composition courses in high school and college, it seems strange that letterwriting should become a lost art.

One excuse for long-distance calls is that people like to hear the voices of those they care about. (I don't. To me it's upsetting and frustrating to try conversing with the disembodied voice of someone I know I cannot be *with*. It's definitely *not* "the next best thing to being there.") It would seem that a much better idea than telephoning would be correspondence by tape. Excellent small tape recorders are available these days at very reasonable prices, and a three-inch tape costs no more to mail than a letter. The beauty of a tape is that the recipient can listen to your voice when *he* wants to, and as many times as he likes. What's more, it will sound a lot more like you than your voice does over the phone.

Properly used, the telephone is a great convenience, of course; but I think it's time that somebody pointed out that it can also be a confounded nuisance. The next time you contemplate a long-distance call, ask yourself if a postcard wouldn't do just as well. Nine times out of ten it probably would.

HURRAY FOR FREEDOM

Several years ago a rumor was going around that a group of anti-war protesters and radical types were planning a massive "freedom rally" in the small town of Freedom, Wyoming. The liberals heaped scorn on its citizens for not wanting a freedom rally in Freedom. Since many liberals seem to believe in the right to push people around for the sake of what they consider good causes and I believe in the right of people not to be pushed around, I defended the good people of Freedom:

"Hurray for Freedom, Wyoming! Why should Freedom or any other community suffer itself to be swamped by an invasion of people it does not want? Why shouldn't communities as well as individuals have a right to privacy, the right to be let alone? Isn't that what our ancestors came here for in the first place?

"I would be the last to deny anybody's right to visit Freedom, Wyoming, or anyplace else. But the organized invasion of a small community by large masses of people is a somewhat different matter than an exercise of individual liberties, because now you are infringing on the rights and liberties of the community being invaded. I am not defending the political views of the people of Freedom—I suspect I would disagree with them strongly—but I am defending what seems to be a lost cause in this country: the right of people not to be harassed and molested."

A MATTER OF TASTE

Pornography is supposed to be that which appeals to prurient interest; but then, so does the Bible. What's wrong with appealing to prurient interest anyway? We Americans are a prurient people. (Look at the way we're always "cracking down on smut" when people with better things to do wouldn't even bother about it.) So why deny our own culture? Nobody is compelled to watch blue movies or read sexy books, but these arts flourish because they are what a lot of Americans like. They have as much right to indulge their tastes as anyone else so long as they don't try to impose them on others.

I am not defending pornography, which is usually rather dull garbage, anyway. I am not even arguing about freedom of the press. I am defending the right of privacy, the right of people in a free country not to have society sticking its nose into their personal lives. It is preposterous that a free country should have laws about what people read, and the number of judicial man-years that have been wasted over such trivia is a disgrace to this nation. In a world beset by real problems, this is indeed fiddling while the city goes up.

It is not the proper business of government to legislate morality or arbitrate tastes. There does not seem to have been any massive breakdown of Danish morality since Denmark threw out these ridiculous statutes altogether.* In so doing, this small country has shown far better sense than the mighty U.S.

Even so, while censorship and book banning have no place in a free country, an acceptable compromise might be to rate books the way we do movies. The sale of X-rated books, like that of whiskey, could be forbidden to minors; and the ratings would enable those with squeamish tastes to avoid what they might find offensive. Furthermore, booksellers would have clear guidelines for handling their wares and compliance with these would protect them from harassment by overzealous police. Most important of all, however,

* Bert Kutchinsky, Director of the Institute of Criminal Science at the University of Copenhagen, reports a dramatic *decrease* in sex crimes as a result of the open availablity of pornography. See *Psychology Today*, November, 1973.

would be the preservation of the right of adult citizens in a free country to read what they choose.

LINGUISTICS: NIHILISM OR SCIENCE?

True language seems to be a uniquely human achievement, but it is an evolutionary one—like having a brown or black or white skin or walking erect and using tools with the hands. To be sure, we can contrive artificial languages like Esperanto or Fortran and make up our own rules for how they should work, just as we can make robots and program their workings. But about all we can do with such evolutionary products of nature as man and his speech is try to find out how they do work.

Language is a complex, highly structured activity, and its workings are governed by definite rules. But its structure was not imposed by grammarians, and its rules are not the ones that school-marms and purists make up, any more than the law of gravitation was something that Isaac Newton made up.

Actually, many of our "rules of grammar" don't describe grammar at all. They are prescriptions for linguistic etiquette. Grammatically, double negatives, sentences ending in prepositions, and split infinitives are historically sound and perfectly intelligible features of English; but somewhere along the line there has been foisted upon us the notion that such usages are uncouth or "bad English" or not the way nice people talk. Despite the fact that they are the way lots of nice people talk—and furthermore, make themselves perfectly clear—these notions persist. It is these unscientific, unrealistic rules of etiquette masquerading as grammar that sometimes try the patience of linguists.

Hayakawa once said that the lexicographer is a historian, not a lawgiver. The linguist, likewise, is an anthropologist, not a policeman. He is not some sort of nihilist saying, "Down with the rules! Just do your own thing." He is a scientist trying to find out what the rules really are.

"I AIN'T NEVER HAD NONE NEITHER"

In what way is this bad English? In what way is it good? I asked these questions on an exam; and my students, at least, knew the answers. Most of us, alas, know about as much about our own language as a Victorian maiden was supposed to know about sex.

Double and even quadruple negatives were perfectly good English until an eighteenth-century clergyman named Robert Lowth set himself up as a grammarian. He knew about as much about how languages actually work as a second-grader today, but people took his word for things because he was a bishop. One of the sillier rules that he made up was the one which says that two negatives cancel each other. In other European languages, and in the less inhibited vernacular of our own, two, three, or four negatives merely reinforce one another. (After all, -2 and -3 don't make plus anything; they make -5.)

Now, "I ain't never had none neither" is perfectly good English in the sense that it serves the purpose of language, which is communication. To no one who heard it would there be the slightest doubt as to what the speaker meant. Because of the notions foisted upon us by people like Lowth, however, we say that it is "bad English"—it is no acceptable usage in polite society; it ain't couth; it's not the way nice people talk.

But my kids talk that way, and they are nice people. Unfortunately, however, they are going to have to live with the spiritual descendants of Lowth rather than with linguists like me. Still, I would rather concentrate on having them make themselves clear. We can rely on both the schools and their peers to harass them sufficiently about the social gaucheries in their speech.

I'm still convinced, though, that had this kind of linguistic snobbery prevailed in Shakespeare's day, his poems and plays would have been a good deal less than immortal. Those of Lowth's contemporaries certainly are.

We liberals are well aware that many people's notions about black people, the women's liberation movement, or sex education are based on superstitions, prejudices, and old wives' tales rather than

85

on facts. Yet we still regard all sorts of unscientific pedagogical nonsense as facts about language.

A typical notion is that pedagogical policing is responsible for the uniformity of American English over the vast area of our nation. Actually, this resulted from the comparatively recent and unusually rapid growth of our country, plus the mobility of our people, our swift transportation, our mass media, and our means of instantaneous nationwide communication, none of which existed during the growth of the world's older nations.

There is, of course, such a thing as linguistic etiquette, silly as it may seem to a rational linguist. Certain expressions in the vernacular do offend certain people, and there is no harm in calling the attention of the young to this fact. But let us get straight what it is we are talking about. Let us not confuse Dr. Kinsey or Masters and Johnson with Emily Post. Let us not try to pass off our notions of propriety as facts about the structure of English.

WHAT'S WRONG WITH CIRCULARITY?

I have been reading Philip Tartaglia's *Problems in the Construction of a Theory of Natural Language,* * in which he discusses various efforts to find ways of explaining how languages work that are neither circular nor intuitive. Linguists worry a lot about circularity, by which they mean "talking in circles" or defining a thing in terms of itself, because they find it very hard to get away from this vice. This is because language is not only what the linguist is talking about, but is also the means by which he talks about it. (As for intuition, no matter how hard the logicians try to find infallible ways of saying what anything actually is or actually means, our judgements of what is or is not grammatical or meaningful or linguistically valid seem ultimately to depend on our intuitive "feel" for what makes sense and what doesn't.)

One idea for getting away from circularity is to devise a scientifically precise and logical "metalanguage" (like Fortran, Cobol, and the like which are used in programming computers) as a way of describing natural language by some means other than itself. (We see this sort of thing in the quasi-algebraic formulas of the transformational grammarians.) This is not wholly successful, because such a metalanguage is still a language and, like mathematics, has natural language as its ultimate base.

Tartaglia says, "A theory attempting to explicate the linguistic intuition of a speaker cannot appeal to the linguistic intuition of a speaker." The question I want to raise is, Why not? Let us for a moment consider the toolmaker, whose craft in some ways resembles that of the linguist, because a toolmaker uses tools to make other tools and relies on his intuition, that is, on his feel for how tools function, to succeed in his task. If we told him that it was "unscientific" to use his lathes and milling machines and micrometers, and his experience with these tools, to make other lathes, milling machines, and micrometers, he would say we were crazy. Both circularity and intuition are indispensable to the accomplishment of his job (another word for them is "feedback") and, if we will think

* The Hague: Mouton and Company, 1972.

about it a little, to any other human achievement. What makes linguists feel they have to be different?

I do not propose circularity as a discovery procedure for revealing any basic new truths about language; but on the other hand, I would not reject it as altogether pernicious or useless. Here are some shamelessly circular definitions that I used in my course in American English linguistics:

"A construction is a meaningful sequence of words between whose major constituents there is a syntactic relationship."

"Syntax is what the constituents of a construction have to do with each other; for example, the relationship between subject and predicate, or between a verb and its object, is a syntactic relationship."

"The constituents of a construction are the two major parts of it between which there is a syntactic relationship."

Obviously, these contributed nothing exciting to linguistic theory; but, together with other material, they did help my students to understand construction-and-constituent grammar.

Our task is to increase man's understanding of what languages consist of and how they work. This is no small undertaking; and it would seem that anything we have going for us, including circularity and intuition, if they will help, should be used. I do not maintain that we should rely only on these, or that efforts to find some vantage point outside language, from which we can view it objectively, should not continue; but until the latter are more successful than they have been to date, let us not scorn any aids to understanding we have.

THE CIVIL WAR

The struggle for Black freedom continues to this very hour.
It was not won in any sense at all by the Civil War.
                                        —Donald Szantho Harrington

The last time that Americans fought for liberty was in the Civil War—and the side that fought for it lost. The twentieth-century civil rights struggle should suffice to remind us that the liberation of the Negro was one thing the Union victory did *not* achieve. What it did do was wreck the federal system which the founders of our country established as a bulwark against the abuses of centralized power.

Was preserving the Union really worth all that bloodshed and bitterness? The Confederate States would have made a nice country; in fact, there is enough territory here to make half a dozen nice countries. Instead, we have sold our libertarian birthright for a mess of imperialist pottage. We have forsaken the American dream to become a monstrosity like the Roman Empire or the Soviet Union—and the Negro is still fighting for rights which, as a Confederate citizen, he might have won long ago, for the Old South had loved him as the North never did.

We must remember that the generation of Southerners who fought the Civil War did not bring slavery to these shores—any more than the present generation of New Yorkers or Californians produced Harlem and Watts. Slavery was already here. The Civil War South was stuck with an institution which it had inherited and which was nearly as widely deplored in the South as the North. In fact, a Southern state was the first to prohibit the slave trade, and the Confederate constitution explicitly banned it.

In the modern South, the Negro has known segregation and been able to overcome it by nonviolent means; but in the North, he has known the total isolation of such ghettos as Harlem, Detroit, Chicago, and Watts. It is his plight here—in the North which is supposed to have liberated him—that has driven him to desperate riots and Black Power.

I do not have the answers to complex racial problems, but being more honest with ourselves ought to help. Relieving ourselves of the myth that we fought a major war just to end slavery would be a good place to start.

BLACK CULTURE

The Jews have had a literature, a faith, and a language of their own for two thousand years. The Navaho Indians still have their own land, their own language, and their own customs. But the Black American, through no fault of his own, is in a cultural limbo. When his ancestors were brought to this country as slaves, they were cut off totally from their African roots. For over a century the only language they have known has been English, and the only culture they have known has been American culture. But because of their status as slaves or second-class citizens on the American scene, American culture is not really theirs either.

Black Americans have what it takes to create a truly fine culture of their own, but from what will they create it? We all like to know where our ancestors come from, and they take the same kind of interest in Africa that I do in Scotland; yet at this late date to pretend that we *are* Scotchmen or Africans would be pretty absurd. We're all Americans now, but just as the Navaho Americans and the Jewish Americans are their own kind of Americans, with their own traditions and culture, so now the Black Americans want to be *their* own kind of Americans with a culture they can call their own. In fact, it has become something of an academic fad to pretend that they've already got it. Certainly they've made some excellent beginnings, but it seems to me that for the most part it is still in a state of becoming, something they have just begun to create.

"Rediscovering their African heritage," alas, won't do much for them, because they've been out of touch with it for a couple of centuries and not much about it is any longer relevant to them. How many Black Americans today, for instance, can tell whether or not their ancestors lived in the glorious Empire of Mali? There may be a few elements in the various African cultures to which they can still relate, but I think the new Black American culture will have to come mostly from their experience as an evolving people in the New World.

Is limbo perhaps "where it's at"? Novels by such authors as Baldwin, Wright, Ellison, and Wideman are about Black people;

91

but they are still American literature that can be enjoyed by people like me, not merely because of the insight they give into the Black American experience, but because they're good reading. Do Black Americans really want to create a literature so ethnic, so uniquely Black, that it will be of interest only to cultural anthropologists and other Black people? (Ishmael Reed's *Mumbo-Jumbo* struck me as somewhat this kind of book.) Maybe some of them do; but if it's their gain, it's America's loss.

I find few prospects so dismal as that of a culturally homogenized America. I wish our Black neighbors well in their struggle to create their own thing, but I hope they can do it without having to withdraw completely from the American scene.

It's their country, too.

BUSSING

Arbitrarily imposed integration and arbitrarily imposed segregation are equally bad, because in either case you are infringing on the right of people to live as they wish. The great injustice of American history has been that our ethnic minorities have not been enjoying this right, but I don't think the answer lies in depriving the rest of us of it.

"Hauling schoolchildren hither and yon just to mix up the races is as stupid as hauling them hither and yon just to keep the races apart. Integration for its own sake is a cop-out for liberals who like to make a racial issue out of what ought to be an educational one. 'Relieving racial imbalance' has a nice sociological ring to it, and it saves us the bother of coping with the real problems."

A statement like the above, which I made in my column in the *Laramie Sentinel,* could easily be misquoted or quoted out of context to prove that I am a racist. If I am, then so are the Blacks, Chicanos, Indians, and Chinese who have often protested the bussing arrangements as bitterly as anyone else.

The trouble with bussing and other schemes for "achieving racial balance" is that they focus attention on the very racial differences that we have been struggling so hard to deemphasize. Sorting children out on the basis of race and sending them to schools far from their neighborhoods because of what color they were is precisely what was wrong about segregation. Now, in the name of integration, we want to do the same thing.

Integration can never succeed as long as it is just something that we impose on white people or something that we try to do for black people. Since it involves both races, it can only succeed where both races want it to succeed. Whether the kids in a given school are all black or all white or some of each shouldn't matter. What *does* matter is how good an education they get.

Bussing may be justifiable as a temporary measure to assure equality of educational opportunity in some cases. But let us be wary of those who would substitute arbitrary "racial balance" arrangements for justice, equality, and the right of all American children to decent schooling wherever they happen to live.

BACK WHERE THEY CAME FROM?

History may repeat itself, but it rarely reverses itself. My Indian friends might tell me that I do not belong here, that this is not my country, and that I ought to go back where I came from. But where would that be? This is where I came from. My people have been in this country for three hundred and fifty years, and I'm staying. White supremacists may feel that our Black neighbors should go back to Africa. Well, when slavery in the land of the free was still young, some of them did and founded Liberia; but now, a century and a half later, America is where they came from, too.

Now take an Israeli kid who was born and raised in Palestine, whose mother tongue is Hebrew, and who has never known any other home. How do you tell him that he doesn't belong there, that it is not his country, and that he should leave? Suppose we grant that the Palestinian Arabs got a raw deal, even as the American Indians did, and we concede that the State of Israel should never have been allowed to happen; what do we do about that young Israeli?

Israel *has* happened. Like the U.S.A., it has been rough on the natives, but it is there. It is a fact of history and it's not about to just go away. For better or for worse, its neighbors are going to have to live with it.

WHAT IS A UNIVERSITY FOR?

I have heard it said, and by a noted educator at that, that the purpose of higher education is to teach people how to think. It's no wonder our educational establishment is in trouble, if it must waste its time teaching one how to think! One should have learned that in kindergarten. Surely our universities have better reasons for being, but I think they differ from the reasons the students attend them.

A cat comes into the world equipped with the full set of instincts he needs to operate as a cat. There is very little that he needs to learn. And, as psychologists and anthropologists from Freud to Ardrey have reminded us, instinct plays a part in human life, too. But what is unique about man, according to Alfred Korzybski, is that he is a "time-binder." He has evolved a culture that he receives from his predecessors, modifies a little during his brief life-span, and passes on to his descendants. We benefit not only from the wisdom of Einstein and Schweitzer, but also from the wisdom of Lao-tse and Jesus. We know how to build spaceships because our great-grandfathers knew how to build steamships.

So basic to man's survival is the time-binding function that he has set up special institutions to carry it out, and presumably he has staffed them with experts. The task with which he has charged them is no less than this: *to pass on the culture*. How well do they do it?

How many of us have seen a germ cause disease? What evidence of our own senses tells us that the earth is not stationary and flat and that the sun does not move across the sky? Who among us has counted the inhabitants of Wyoming? When was the last time you saw a radio wave enter your television set? Yet we take as axiomatic such facts as that germs cause disease, that the earth spins on its axis and goes around the sun, that about 340,000 people live in Wyoming, and that electromagnetic waves bring our favorite spectator sport into our living rooms. We believe this information to be true because it has been passed on to us by people whom we have reason to believe we can trust.

Why have so many of us come to distrust the educational establishment though we take on trust so much of the information it gives us? Our teachers, by and large, are sincere, honest people. The trouble is not that what they tell us is unreliable or untrue. The trouble is that it is irrelevant. It may not be irrelevant to the purpose for which a college thinks it exists, or to the purpose for which the professors think they are there. But it is irrelevant to the purpose for which most of the students are there.

They are there because American business has debased the college degree by making it a requirement for almost any job that business can offer. A bachelor's degree, when I obtained mine, certified that its holder was an educated man, a custodian of the culture. Today it has been degraded to a mere union card, the ticket that one needs to get in—or at best a certificate of competence in some everyday skill. Our universities are degenerating into mere trade schools, not because the professors want it that way, but because the students do; and the students want it that way because their prospective employers do. They are not looking for an education, but for training in skills which can earn them a living.

Now training in useful skills is something we need very badly, but I do not believe that it is the function of a university to provide it. It is the function of trade schools to provide it. Our country swarms with third-rate lawyers, fourth-rate engineers, fifth-rate artists, and incomprehensible poets, while it is in desperate need of first-rate electronic technicians, appliance repairmen, cement finishers, backhoe operators, auto mechanics, veterinarians, machinists, and welders. Ninety percent of the work in this country, including most engineering, could be done by graduates of any good trade school. We need more and better trade schools to train them, and their certificates of competence in their skills should be honored as much as a college degree. Has it ever occurred to you that a first-class television repairman needs as much knowledge and skill as a doctor? If you don't believe that, take a good look inside your TV set sometime.

It is getting late, but I think that our universities can still become what they once were, the custodians of the culture and the institutions for passing it on. If we continue to degrade them to where they no longer do this because it is no longer what we want them to do, we will end up as a nation of skilled but uneducated technicians.

DOERS AND SCHOLARS

After listening to John Holt I have concluded that there are only two kinds of things people *really* learn: things they need to know, and things they don't need to know. This means that there are two kinds of genuine learners: those Holt calls doers and scholars.

Doers learn what they need to know for the purpose of what they want to do. There is no point in most of us learning how to read a vernier micrometer, but you will soon acquire this skill if you decide to become a machinist. My wife is a far better driver than I am, though I don't think she understands as clearly as I do what goes on under the hood—there's no reason why she should need to. My son is learning how to program a computer to produce such readouts as "Support cohabitation" or "You have just made an unidentified flying statement." He is learning what he needs to know in order to get these results. Only if he wants to design or service computers will he need to learn what goes on inside them. He learns what *he* needs to learn: what kind of input results in what kind of output. How the computer produces the latter is not his affair.

Scholars are people who learn what they don't need to know. They enjoy learning for its own sake. They are curious about how things work whether or not they *need* to know how they work. They study things which they find interesting even if they have no practical use for their knowledge. A little over forty years ago I taught myself to read Yiddish and I still enjoy reading Yiddish, a completely useless skill for a Gentile. (I wouldn't even need to know Yiddish if I was Jewish.) Latin and Greek at least give a scholar some class (which may be why they are called "classical" languages); but even though I dig Yiddish instead, I'm still a scholar.

Now what is wrong with the "new math," which isn't any easier than the old math and doesn't do anything that the old math couldn't do, is that its promoters designed it for scholars. They thought that mathematics would be more interesting and enjoyable if the students could learn, not just how to use numbers, but how numbers work and why they work as they do. The trouble is that most people don't *care* how they work, any more than they care what goes on in a power plant so long as they can turn on a switch and get light.

To study linguistics or write essays and poems, I don't need a slide rule; but I like to work with one, because mathematical concepts intrigue me and the slide rule is a fascinating device. It's nice to have the new math available to people like me who happen to be interested in how numbers work; but for people whose interest in numbers lies only in being able to use them well enough to get a refund on their income tax, it would make better sense to learn how to make one of those neat little electronic calculators do their arithmetic.

Society, of course, is not really divided into doers and scholars; each one of us is. We're doers in some respects and scholars in others. And with regard to many activities, we are both—as I am, for instance, with language or the enthusiast who likes to build up and drive his own dragster is with his car. Education would be a lot more pleasant as well as useful if educators would recognize this and provide different *kinds* of courses in English, mathematics, social science, or physics according to the kind of interest the students have in these subjects. They should be able to take "doer" courses in some, "scholar" courses in others, and both kinds in which they have both kinds of interest.

Most of us can read, write, and speak English well enough for everyday purposes by the time we reach high school; but we might want to learn how to write a decent accident report, a decent love letter, or a decent letter of condolence to a friend upon the death of a child, or a decent letter to apply for a job; and it might help us to learn how to understand the fine print in an insurance policy, the time payment contract on our car, or the mortgage deed on our house. To this end, some sensible grammar might help, but instead, the schools try to teach us transformational grammar or some other fad in which the educational establishment has a vested interest but which is of no value to us whatever unless we happen to be interested in linguistic theory. (If we are, of course, it should be available to us.) If you just want to enjoy listening to music, there is no reason for you to learn how to read it; but you will if you want to become a musician—whether or not they teach you in school.

NO ROOM FOR AMATEURS?

Diane Wakoski, in her column in *American Poetry Review,* has said that the academic world is the only place where there is any poetry anymore. Certainly nearly all of the contributors to this journal are in college English departments, and college campuses are about the only place people read poetry anymore—and then they usually read it only when they have to in order to get their degrees.

Intellectual life on the American campus is healthy enough; what is wrong is that we are getting to where that is the only place where there is any, and monopolies are stifling. (Colleges have poets-in-residence, but did your town ever have one?) Without a Ph.D. in your field, you cannot teach or get your work published no matter how competent a scholar you are. Everything has gotten so specialized and professionalized that it will soon be illegal to help your neighbor unless you have a degree in social work; and unless a writer has attended something like the Iowa Writers' Workshop, he won't stand a chance. Where is there any longer a place for the amateur scholar?

There was a place for him once, and amateurs in the past have enriched our culture to an extent that is barely possible today. Here are just a few of them, with their professions and the amateur work for which they're remembered.

	Profession	*Amateur Field*
Benjamin Lee Whorf	Fire prevention engineer	Linguistics
Wallace Stevens	Insurance executive	Poetry
William Carlos Williams	Physician	Poetry
Charles Ives	Insurance business	Composer
Eric Hoffer	Longshoreman	Sociology
Robert Ardrey	Playwright	Anthropolgy
Lewis Carroll	Mathematician	Children's storie

My particular hero, of course, is Benjamin Whorf, the famous American linguist whose only degree was a B.S. in chemistry and who worked for the Hartford Fire Insurance Company all his life. I, too, am an amateur scholar in the field of linguistics; and my only degree is a B.A. in English. I did teach part-time at the University of Wyoming for a few years when the teacher shortage was so desperate that they couldn't find anyone else. Though I was respected by both colleagues and students and my department head wanted to keep me, I was let go when academically qualified professionals became plentiful. Amateurs were no longer needed, and my little old B.A. from Yale wasn't much of an ornament to the roster.

Since I was only hired for one year and they kept me for seven, which isn't bad for an amateur, I have no regrets and I enjoyed the experience. Besides, it brought me out of the crowded and harassed East to an infinitely more preferable home in Wyoming. But in these affluent times of increased leisure and earlier retirements, I think we will see more amateur scholars with much to offer our cultural life. What troubles me is the question, Who will give them a hearing? How and to whom can they offer their treasures?

NIGHT

Night has always fascinated mankind. We cannot see very well in the dark; so we have peopled it with ghosts and goblins and the mysteries of the unseen. There is also the great quietness of the night, when the clatter of human activities dies down and we hear sounds not of our own making, to remind us that other creatures, some of them terrifying, inhabit our world.

Then, too, the light of day confines us to our own earth, moon, and sun. Only at night can our vision reach beyond them to the rest of the cosmos. Only at night can we study the stars. Our dreams of reaching them and our science fiction that peoples them with strange beings were born of the night.

The night conceals, providing privacy for the intimacies of lovers. Total darkness, though, would be grim; romance flourishes in the soft light of the moon.

Poets have always been inspired by the night, by its mysteries and beauties and wonders. One of Nietzsche's finest rhapsodies is Zarathustra's Night Song:

'Tis night: now do all gushing fountains speak louder,
And my soul also is a gushing fountain.
'Tis night: now do all souls of the loving ones awake.
And my soul also is the soul of a loving one.

Walt Whitman has a lovely and passionate hymn to the night in "Song of Myself":

Press close, bare-bosomed night—press close, magnetic and
    nourishing night!
Night of south winds, night of the large few stars!
Still nodding night—mad naked summer night.
. . . .
Smile, for your lover comes.

Civilization, especially in our garish cities, has enabled us to turn night into day; and we have been proud of that. Perhaps, however, the energy shortage will do more than just teach us to walk again. Perhaps, too, it will give us back the wonder and poetry of the night.

FIREWORKS

In one of my poems* I said:

> ... it's not moonrise
> nor the dawn
> it's the fireworks
> that draw the crowd

Why do they? Watching the fireworks on Ninth Street Hill the other night, I could turn around and see just as impressive a display of brightness and color in the lights of our city. A jet passing overhead or a freight train pulling out of town produces a fine window-shaking roar; yet one small firecracker will get more attention.

The moon and stars on a summer night are more impressive than any man-made display, but they are predictable. They are always there and soon cease to divert us. Were the glorious burst of a Fourth of July aerial bomb to be frozen into a permanent display in the heavens, we would soon get used to it—and it would become a mere tourist attraction.

The fascination of fireworks seems to be in their transitory, momentary, one-of-a-kind nature. What is constant and completely predictable does not fascinate us for long. What we find beautiful is always a little startling; it always embodies an element of surprise.

* "Summer Evenings," in *Ah, But in Casper.*

103

PORT EVERGLADES

I have just returned from a trip down south, *south* of the South, where the wind rarely loses its temper and the Atlantic Ocean sparkles blue and clean in the summery sun. Here at home it is still the tag end of winter. The sky is gray, the air is raw, the grass is brown, and the trees are bare; so my thoughts turn to the few dreamlike days I spent in the city of light, the fabulous city by the sea, baking the Yankee misery out of my bones and healing my frazzled spirit with the company of people I love. And I think of one of the greatest of our simple pleasures and what it is that I enjoy about it so much: going down to Port Everglades and watching the longshoremen unload Renaults and Volkswagens from the *Hilversum* or drums of wire rope and great bundles of some kind of pipe from the *Hakonesan Maru,* or the tall cranes transferring scrap from a train of gondola cars to the hold of a rusty Liberian freighter.

Port Everglades lies broad and open in the sun, and the structural steel awaiting shipment is neatly parked on its flat acres. Its entrance is right on the highway, as inviting as the entrance to Birch State Park up the coast. You drive in and go where you like on the wide, ample roads, and park where you please. You walk about all you want and watch any operation that it strikes your fancy to watch—just the wide, flat land; the roads; some warehouses; and the towering ships where the land meets the sea, and nothing but a breakwater or two between them and Africa. I don't think there is even a fence around the place. It is a public port, and you don't need a pass to roam around it and watch operations to your heart's content. Nobody bothers you, so long as you don't interfere with the work; a longshoreman might ask you politely not to stand in the path of his forklift truck.

Here, wide-open in the Florida sun for anybody who wishes to admire and enjoy without any confounded "security," is a basic and vital operation of commerce; and you can go there whenever you like and watch the actual work being done. Without even asking anybody's permission, you can *see* a car you yourself might conceivably buy come into the country! I am very much taken with Port

Everglades, because things of this kind are very rare in this country. Most of our real work is carried on behind walls and security fences and platoons of guards. Much of what we use is made in windowless factories whose operations are familiar only to the people who work there, and even most of them are familiar with only one little job.

There is a certain unreality to life in this country because the vital workings of our economy are so diligently sealed off from the people. I once drove a steam locomotive on the Lehigh Valley Railroad, as a guest of the engineer. How much chance does a young fellow get to do anything like this today? How much chance does he get to participate, even as a guest, in the vital workings of our economy? Kids used to be able to hang around the blacksmith shop or the roundhouse and learn something about essential work from the people who did it. Now it is very likely that a great many of them will never even see, let alone do, any essential work for their whole lives. But at least, if they can spare the time from doing the frug on the beach, they can go down to Port Everglades and see the longshoremen unloading the ships.

TRAIN WATCHING

When I was attending far-flung Linguistic Society meetings or visiting loved ones in California or Florida, during the last days of the great passenger trains, I traveled in style. I luxuriated in the Sunshine, the New England States, the Chief, the Empire Builder, the City of Los Angeles, the Twentieth Century Limited, and others. I remember them fondly and wonder if the energy shortage and Amtrak, between them, will manage to bring them back. I have a feeling, though, that they will have to remain a memory, like the magnificent dirigibles I saw in my youth.

Though I'm no longer a passenger, I'm still a train watcher, and in our home on the Big Laramie we are ideally situated for that. The main line of the original transcontinental railroad goes just beyond where the river winds through our pasture, and from our living room windows we can view a whole mountain range, a whole sunset—and a whole train on the Union Pacific.

I am not the only one who likes to watch trains. Our guests quickly get hooked. What is it about trains that train watchers watch? Some, especially visitors from the East, are fascinated by the length of our trains and like to count how many cars they have—sometimes more than a hundred. Others are intrigued by their cargo, since much of it is not cooped up in box cars but rides in the open.

We think of Detroit as the auto-manufacturing capital of the world and therefore that all the new cars that travel by rail (and thousands do) should be moving from east to west to their dealers. Not so; just as many new cars travel in the other direction, apparently from Japan or West Coast assembly plants. Automobiles, truck-tractors, lumber, farm machinery, prefabricated sections of bridges, and miles of Pacific Fruit Express cars with California groceries for all America (do they carry nonunion lettuce?) move by our pasture. Whole trainloads of Wyoming coal go by every day to keep the power plants going in Iowa or Wisconsin, and I hope there'll be some left for our fireplace.

Every train has cars in it from railroads all over the continent, and these are what I like to watch. I like to identify as many different railroads as I can and find out where they are (you need an older atlas for this; the new ones show highways instead). Many cars are from very small lines which evidently support themselves by renting out their rolling stock. Do you know what railroad calls itself "The Cotton Belt Route?" Do you know where the Louisville, New Albany, and Corydon Railroad is? The Roscoe, Snyder and Pacific? The San Luis Central? The Pacific Great Eastern?

Maybe the automobile is your thing, or you fly the friendly skies of United, and you don't care. But if you had dined on the Chief or seen the Rockies from the dome car of the Empire Builder, maybe you would.

A CHUNK OF HISTORY

Did you know that the world's first passenger airline was making regularly scheduled flights before World War I? That twenty passengers enjoyed a round-the-world luxury cruise by air only two years after Lindbergh landed in Paris? Or that a commercial airline provided de luxe transatlantic passenger service nearly half a century ago? The aircraft involved were not the Wright brothers' airplanes, but old Count Zeppelin's fabulous dirigibles.

Every American schoolchild knows the story of the Yankee clipper ships, because they were an American triumph. But we remember little of the era of the great airships, possibly because they were a German achievement and Germany was our enemy in both the world wars. But I grew up during that era. To a spectator from the ground there is nothing very impressive about a jet transport in flight because it flies so high and so fast that all you see are the jet trails streaked across the sky. But the great airships sailed majestically along at eighty or ninety miles per hour and only a few hundred feet up.

The three American-built ones all came to bad ends, and we gave up on dirigibles, but I saw them all in their prime. Looking up at a vast silvery shape as big as the *Queen Elizabeth,* filling half the sky and gliding quietly over the rooftops, was a thrill I will remember for the rest of my life—and one which my children, alas, will never experience.

Michael M. Mooney's book *The Hindenburg* (Bantam Books, 1973) is not just the story of that famous ship, but of the whole era of lighter-than-air transport. It brought back to me vividly a time through which I had lived and a chunk of history we had all but forgotten. Nostalgia for the Age of Sail is still strong in thousands of seafaring hearts, but how many today still recall the great airships?